Hello, Helpers

By Janice Behrens

ISBN: 978-1-338-88867-6

Editor: Liza Charlesworth
Art Director: Tannaz Fassihi; Designer: Tanya Chernyak
Photos ©: 2: wavebreakmedia/Shutterstock.com. All other photos © Getty Images.

1 2 3 4 5 6 7 8 9 10   68   31 30 29 28 27 26 25 24 23
Printed in Jiaxing, China. First printing, January 2023.

SCHOLASTIC INC.

Many people help in our town.
Let's wave to them
as we go around.

There is a crossing guard.
She holds a stop sign.
Hello, helper!

There is a firefighter.
He rides in the truck.
Hello, helper!

There is a mail carrier.
She brings the mail.
Hello, helper!

There is a baker.
He bakes yummy bread.
Hello, helper!

There is a construction worker.
She hammers a nail.
Hello, helper!

There is a teacher.
She helps, too.
She reads a book to me and you!